# Not Enough You

## A People-Pleaser's Journal for Recapturing Your Value and Worth

ILENE S. COHEN, PH.D.

HARTE & CO PUBLISHING · MIAMI, FLORIDA

*Not Enough You: A People-Pleaser's Journal for Recapturing Your Value and Worth*

by Ilene S. Cohen, Ph.D.



Published by Harte & Co Publishing



Editor: Denise Fournier

Book design: BookSavvyStudio.com

Printed Edition: ISBN: 978-0-9993115-4-7

First Edition

Printed in the United States of America

*To you — for deciding to do something for yourself*

*I was always going to let someone down, so I decided it wouldn't be me anymore.*

*~Unknown*

# Introduction

DO YOU HAVE A TOUGH TIME SAYING NO? Do you struggle with thinking you might be letting people down? Have you found yourself wishing you could make yourself a priority but don't quite know how to do it? If so, I feel your frustration. I know how hard it can be to live your life that way, never feeling good enough, continually feeding an impulse to please, and finding it hard to say no to others and yes to your needs. Life isn't just complicated, it's straight-up paralyzing at times—particularly when you're trying to be what everyone else expects you to be. But you're likely to find that even if you comply with everyone's wishes and whims, they still won't be happy. And, of course, you won't be either! Welcome to the paradox of relationships; welcome to the deception of people-pleasing.

This is why it's essential to do some of the difficult work of reflecting on your own life, so you can make the changes that will finally let you live in your own truth. This journal includes quotes from my award-winning self-help book, *When it's Never About You*, along with other important quotes, activities, and questions for you to ponder in your efforts to become less of a people-pleaser and more of your own self. This journal will give you the time and space you need to focus on your own life. It will allow you to look within yourself and start being more intentional with your life. So, what are you waiting for? Let's start creating less "YES" and more "YOU" in your life!

*People-pleasers tend to believe that doing things for other people- whether be their family members, friends, or co-workers- is a requirement for being a good, nice, and responsible person.*

1. Do you believe that by acting in pleasing ways, you'll be immune to criticism, hurt, or rejection?
   ☐ Yes ☐ No

2. Do you avoid confrontation at all costs?
   ☐ Yes ☐ No

3. Do you stuff down your pain to avoid disagreeing with someone? ☐ Yes ☐ No

4. Do you have a tough time dealing with other people's negative reactions? ☐ Yes ☐ No

If you answered "yes" to any of these questions, what would you like to change if you knew you didn't have to be afraid?

*It's not selfish to love yourself, take care of yourself, and make your happiness a priority. It's necessary.*

~ Mandy Hale

You probably believe that it's selfish to consider your needs first. But, if you could stop thinking of it as selfish to put yourself first, what changes would you make in your life?

*Never apologize for wanting what you want, asking for what you need, or for stating your boundaries.*

*Real change begins with the awareness that we create our sense of self within our relationships, not apart from them.*

Many of the personal choices we make shape how we think and lead us to make meaningful changes in our lives. All these significant changes start with awareness. Your ability to develop self-awareness might be thwarted by your resistance to being viewed as selfish.

How can you shift your focus from others to yourself without believing that you're being selfish?

*No matter your age, circumstance, race, sex, or religion, now is the time to stop the cycle of people-pleasing. Living to please others is draining, lonely, and damaging to your health.*

List 4 ways that people-pleasing has negatively affected your life.

1. ______________________________

______________________________

______________________________

______________________________

______________________________

2. ______________________________

______________________________

______________________________

______________________________

______________________________

3. ______________________________

______________________________

______________________________

______________________________

______________________________

4. ______________________________

______________________________

______________________________

______________________________

______________________________

*Life isn't just complex; it's straight-up paralyzing at times—particularly when you're trying to be what everyone else expects you to be.*

Honestly answer the questions below:

1. Do I have a tough time saying no out of fear that I will hurt others? ☐ Yes ☐ No

2. Do I struggle with thinking I might be letting people down? ☐ Yes ☐ No

3. Do I find myself wishing I could make myself a priority but am unsure how to do it? ☐ Yes ☐ No

4. Do I continuously put others' needs before my own? ☐ Yes ☐ No

5. Do I comply with everyone's wishes and whims, only to find that they stay unhappy? ☐ Yes ☐ No

6. Am I happy and living my life the way I want to? ☐ Yes ☐ No

*Normalize saying "No" without feeling guilty and saying sorry.*

*People who go through life people-pleasing don't challenge common beliefs about what people should do or how they ought to behave; instead, they take them on as true.*

Open your mind and start challenging the beliefs and ideas that got you into the people-pleasing position. Challenge the ideas that don't match your experiences.

Ask yourself:

What ideas are getting in my way of putting myself first?

What do I believe will happen if I put myself first?

What decisions can I start making to have more freedom of choice in my life?

*Ideas and beliefs are very powerful, because most of us go around treating them as facts and truths.*

*I lost myself in trying
to find ways to keep
everyone else happy.*

Do you value calmness and relaxation? Do you try to avoid drama and conflict, aiming to keep the peace in your relationships as much as possible? Think about how much of yourself you've lost in your efforts to keep everyone else happy.

List 5 things you would do if you weren't trying to keep the peace:

1. ______________________________

______________________________

______________________________

2. ______________________________

______________________________

______________________________

3. ______________________________

______________________________

______________________________

4. ______________________________

______________________________

______________________________

5. ______________________________

______________________________

______________________________

*"What you heal in yourself,*
*you heal for your entire family line."*

~ Chani Nicholas

Our culture is centered on the belief that selfless people are doing the right thing. Insinuating that people who give all of themselves are immune to struggle and difficulty.

The truth is that all people, regardless of how much they give, have problems. It's okay to feel depressed, lonely, and overwhelmed.

Write about the difference it would make in your life if you were okay with not being okay all the time:

*Before you try to fix someone else's vibe,*
*make sure you're not killing your own in the process.*
*Protect your energy first.*

Self-fullness:
Striking a healthy balance that will allow you to stay connected and kind to others in a way that also allows you to prioritize your own needs.

You've probably already figured out that trying to make everyone else happy while forgetting about yourself is a tireless, thankless, and fruitless effort. Think about how you can strike a workable balance between selfishness and selflessness.

List 5 things you've put aside for others that you can start doing for yourself:

1. ______________________________

______________________________

______________________________

2. ______________________________

______________________________

______________________________

3. ______________________________

______________________________

______________________________

4. ______________________________

______________________________

______________________________

5. ______________________________

______________________________

______________________________

*Always doing for others at your own expense doesn't automatically translate to having a life of value.*

*You cannot solve a*
*problem from the same*
*consciousness that*
*created it.*
*You must learn to*
*see the world anew.*

*~Albert Einstein.*

When you hyper-focus on others, you miss out on your own life. Going through life people-pleasing is kind of like sleepwalking; you're going through the motions, but you aren't connected to your true self.

Think about the roles you play within your relationships, and write about the ways you hyper-focus on others or disconnect from your true self.

*It's easy for people-pleasers to give others control of their lives, only to wonder later why they're always dissatisfied, depleted, and surrounded by demanding people.*

When you're guided by a desire to please, your self-worth gets tangled up with how much you do for others and how good you are at making others happy and comfortable. This makes it hard to change, because the thought of doing things differently invites fear about how other people will react. Think about some things you can do to manage your anxiety when you start speaking your truth.

Write about how you can respond to your emotions differently:

*Although it might seem counterintuitive, prioritizing your needs and gaining a strong sense of self is better for your relationships because it serves to strengthen them.*

The ingredients for healthy human connection (authenticity, honesty, intimacy, etc.) won't come together if you don't participate actively in your relationships. Think of ways you can speak up when you're angry, hurt, or feel violated.

What are some communication skills you need to work on? Place a check mark next to the areas you want to improve:

- ☐ Communicate More Clearly
- ☐ Be More Honest
- ☐ Speak Up More Before I Get Angry
- ☐ Calm Myself Down More Effectively
- ☐ Stay Connected with People
- ☐ Remain Clear in the Face of Pressure
- ☐ Speak My Mind
- ☐ Approach Situations with Confidence

List some of your own:

*Self-fullness means knowing that you are only responsible for yourself.*

Many people-pleasers feel responsible for other people's feelings. How freeing would it be for you to work on feeling responsible only for yourself and how you feel?

Write about what your life would look like if you no longer believed that you're responsible for other people:

*If you let it, your fear will keep you paralyzed, holding you prisoner in a life that isn't yours.*

Instead of waiting for something or someone else to allow you to live a more self-full life, give yourself permission to start doing it today.

List the fears that get in your way of focusing more on yourself.

List the ways that you can break free from those fears:

*Lasting growth begins with learning to observe ourselves in our relationships, being aware that problems do not reside within individuals, but rather in the interconnection between them.*

We think that taking responsibility means taking the blame; and since it makes us anxious to feel blamed, we aim to reduce our anxiety by placing blame elsewhere. But the truth is, this doesn't solve anything.

How can you take responsibility for your challenges and actions without taking the blame?

How can you become more self-aware when challenges arise?

*Our mindset contains our ideas, beliefs, and views about life. Our previous experiences of the world shape it along with ideas passed down from generations before.*

The perceptions we form about our past influence our present and future experiences, thereby creating our reality. Think about some of the beliefs you hold that haven't been serving you.

List 4 ways that these beliefs impact your actions.

1. ______________________________

2. ______________________________

3. ______________________________

4. ______________________________

*The past does not necessarily cause the issues we face in the present; rather, the recreation of a problem that was shaped in the past creates a problem in the present.*

*~ Michael Kerr, MD*

Situations that took place within the families we were born into have a way of repeating themselves if we don't do something about them.

- Have you noticed any patterns in your own family?
- Can you identify personal problems, health issues, relationship cut-offs, and/or addictions that have made their way down your family tree?

Take note of the patterns you notice.

*Becoming self-full means abandoning the belief that you need to put other people's needs before your own to have peaceful relationships.*

Think about how you formed the idea that in order to have peaceful relationships, you need to give in and roll over. Think deeply about whether this idea still fits with what you truly believe.

Ask yourself:

Did I have a very reactive parental figure?

Was I punished for having a different opinion from others?

*Although you can't always control what happens to you, you can control what you do about it.*

Sit silently for 15 minutes. Take inventory of how you can better express yourself in moments of stress. Consider how you can maintain your sanity while others react to you.

Write about what you can maintain control over as you surrender control over what others think, say, or do.

*While she was escaping
conflict on the outside,
she was caught in a
battle within.*

When you avoid trying to disappoint people, you continuously compromise your time, values, and perceived self-worth. Think about someone you're afraid of disappointing.

Ask yourself:

How can I be honest with myself and others about how I want to spend my time?

How can I remember my value, even when others put me down?

*She prioritized pleasing others and avoided confrontation, criticism, and ridicule by ignoring her own needs.*

Think about what you notice when you take the time to observe your own life. Ask yourself: Is my need to please automatic?

How do I manage the negative emotions that come with life's many disappointments?

*Stop planting flowers in other people's yards*
*if they aren't going to water them.*

*When you change the way you look at things, the things you look at change.*

*~ Wayne Dyer*

Until you start seeing and thinking about things differently, you'll continue feeling stuck right where you are. If you want something to change and you want to move forward in life, it's time to start writing a new story about your life—one that's based on a mindset of self-fullness rather than selflessness.

Rewrite your story here:

*Men are not prisoners of fate, but only prisoners of their own minds.*

*~Franklin D. Roosevelt*

With no sense of purpose or self-confidence, you can easily succumb to being the person who always does for others. What gives you a sense of purpose and self-confidence?

Write your responses in BIG, colorful letters.

*"Care about people's approval, and you will always be their prisoner."*

~LAO TZU

*My goal shouldn't have been to work on becoming a better problem solver. Instead, I should have been working on learning to stop doing things for others so they could start doing it for themselves.*

How could you learn to be with the discomfort you feel when you aren't helping others, instead of automatically running to help them out?

What could you do to shift your focus from others to yourself?

*If I say no to someone and they get angry, it doesn't mean I should've said yes.*

*Acute anxiety is fed by fear of what is; chronic anxiety is fed by fear of what might be.*

~ Murray Bowen

Think of something that's currently bothering you and write about it here. You don't have to try to solve it. Just focus on getting your fears out of your head and onto the page.

*Sometimes in life, we take a stand. We take a good, hard look at our lives and decide it's time to change. Sometimes we find ourselves in circumstances that force us to figure out what we need to do next, instead of what we have always done.*

There's real wisdom in feeling, thinking about, and becoming aware of your sadness instead of hiding from the pain. There's growth in falling, in hurting, in accepting the pain.

Write about a life struggle that helped you open your mind and change your perspective.

When aspects of
ourselves are distanced,
denied, or devalued,
they'll always try to
make us listen by
surfacing as unwanted
symptoms.

Circle the symptoms you experience regularly:

| | | | |
|---|---|---|---|
| Headaches | anxiety | depression | muscle pain |
| feeling lost | fatigue | burnout | restlessness |
| panic attacks | trouble sleeping | | |

Name some of your own symptoms, and write about what they would tell you if they could talk:

*Don't be afraid of losing people; be afraid of losing yourself by trying to please everyone around you.*

*The people in our lives are here to teach us, challenge us and help us grow.*

We blame others for our problems, which keeps us from taking a look at ourselves.

Instead of seeing others as the source of your problems, how can you use your relationships as a source of change and growth?

How can you better define yourself in your most important relationships?

*Whatever you are not changing, you are choosing.*

You'll realize that you alone are responsible for your happiness and that this is true for every human being on the planet; other people's happiness isn't your responsibility.

Remember, you still deserve to be loved when you:

- ✔ Don't feel happy
- ✔ Aren't perfect
- ✔ Can't be helpful to someone
- ✔ Don't get it right
- ✔ Make a mistake

I deserve to feel loved when...

*Once you realize that you don't have the power to make someone else happy—that you can only create happiness for yourself by changing the way you view the world—everything changes.*

Think about how you can hold people accountable for their own lives, allowing them to be in control of their problems. What would you be doing if you didn't feel responsible for other people's lives?

*When we wonder if others accept us, we rely on them to tell us who we are.*

*Every time you are tempted to react in the same old way, ask if you want to be a prisoner of the past or a pioneer of the future.*

*~Deepak Chopra*

If you recognize that you're doing all the heavy lifting in your relationships, here are some quick tips to consider:

- Become aware of when you're handling your own tasks or taking on tasks that other people should be doing.
- Take note of the things you're failing to do for yourself.
- Practice sitting with the discomfort that comes with letting others deal with their own issues.
- Hold back from trying to manage other people's responsibilities.
- If you're used to being the person who fixes everything when anxiety is high, try to be aware of that, and hold yourself back from repeating old patterns.

List some of your own behaviors to pay attention to:

*When tension mounts at work or in any relationship system, there are those who react to the tension with lowered energy levels and those, like myself, who react with increased energy. It's easy to think that the increased energy is a positive thing, but because it's driven by anxiety, it gets directed in unhelpful ways which get in the way of others working well.*

*– Jenny Brown, MSW*

Ask yourself:

When did I first start believing I needed to please others to be a good person?

Who in my life would agree that I'm a people-pleaser?

What would I prefer to be thinking, feeling, or doing instead of pleasing others?

*"Time spent in self-reflection is never wasted. It is an intimate date with yourself."* ~ Paul TP Wong

*When we don't have a sense of self, our goal is to figure out what our environment wants us to do.*

When we fail to develop a healthy self, our wellbeing and functioning wind up being dependent on what others say or don't say, instead of being based what we want. Our sense of self vanishes in the presence of others.

List 4 things that automatically bring you joy.

1. ______________________________

______________________________

______________________________

______________________________

2. ______________________________

______________________________

______________________________

______________________________

3. ______________________________

______________________________

______________________________

______________________________

4. ______________________________

______________________________

______________________________

______________________________

*Don't feel bad for making decisions that upset other people. You're not responsible for their happiness; you're responsible for yours.*

*The only way to move through it is together. Emotional distance doesn't help. Learning to manage yourself in the situation of being with the people who bring about stress helps. Be present with your anxiety because backing away creates more of it.*

When an opportunity comes up to please, notice it, and then try to do something different than your usual response. Do something that occupies your time instead of over-functioning for others.

Ask yourself:

What are people doing in my life to pull me back into pleasing behaviors?

If I were to live self-fully, what would be the first sign that a significant change—no matter how small—had occurred?

*People-pleasers are in a constant state of vulnerability, adjusting themselves and their internal functioning to keep other people in harmony. That's why it's important to put boundaries in place and decide what's non-negotiable for you in your relationships.*

When you do too much for other people, your *self* vanishes; you start to become what other people want you to be. Research shows that this kind of behavior can cause chronic inflammation in the body and many other physical symptoms.

List 5 of your non-negotiables in your relationships. Think about ways that you can stick to your boundaries when they're broken.

**1.** ______________________________

______________________________

______________________________

**2.** ______________________________

______________________________

______________________________

**3.** ______________________________

______________________________

______________________________

**4.** ______________________________

______________________________

______________________________

**5.** ______________________________

______________________________

*"Boundaries define us. They define what is me and what is not me. A boundary shows me where I end, and someone else begins, leading me to a sense of ownership. Knowing what I am to own and take responsibility for gives me freedom."*

~HENRY CLOUD

*If someone throws a fit because you set boundaries, it's just more evidence that the boundary is needed.*

*~Unknown*

When people excessively count on others, they learn to always—whether knowingly or unknowingly—recruit people to do things for them. When they run out of options, they have no choice but to start doing for themselves.

How can you keep that in mind when someone you care about is pressuring you to do something you don't want to do?

*"Setting boundaries is a way of caring for myself. It doesn't make me mean, selfish, or uncaring (just) because I don't do things your way. I care about me, too."*

~ Christine Morgan

*We can say what we need to say. We can gently, but assertively, speak our mind. We do not need to be judgmental, tactless, blaming or cruel when we speak our truths.*

*~ Melody Beattie*

It can feel challenging to express ourselves, especially when we've fallen into the pattern of ignoring our own voice.

Who are the people you'd like to communicate with better?

How can you speak your mind and define who you are in your relationships?

*"The privilege of a lifetime is being who you are."*

~ Joseph Campbell

*She was the archetypal selfless mother; living only for her children, sheltering them from the consequences of their actions-and in the end doing them irreparable harm.*

~ Marcia Muller

By attempting to shelter the people we love from the natural process of life, we keep them from developing the strength and resilience they need to overcome challenging circumstances.

Sit and think for 5 minutes about who the people are that you shelter the most in your life. Record some of your thoughts here:

*Feel it. The thing that*
*you don't want to feel.*
*Feel it. And be free.*

*~Nayyirah Waheed*

How you perceive a crisis and decide to respond to it can make the difference between effectively growing from the experience or regressing into old, not so helpful patterns.

What are some things you are avoiding that make you anxious?

List 3 situations where you found the courage to face your fears.

1.

2.

3.

*Crisis can be averted when one can find a person with the courage to define self, who is invested in the welfare of the family as in self, who is neither angry nor dogmatic, whose energy goes to changing self rather than telling others what they should do.*

*~ Murray Bowen*

When a negative situation arises, instead of disconnecting from it immediately by going into thoughtless action, look within yourself and ask, "What type of person do I want to be in this situation?"

*Each circumstance is a gift, and in each experience is hidden treasure.*

*~ Neale Donald Walsch*

When a crisis arises, acting self-fully can allow you to move through setbacks without creating more drama in other aspects of your life. Here are some ways you can do it:

- Make a real effort to have your feelings line up with your logical brain by looking at the facts of the situation.
- Practice sitting with the discomfort that comes from your desires not being immediately satisfied.
- Hold your values as personal, instead of imposing them on other people.
- When people in your family system upset you or disagree with you, try to stay connected to them instead of pulling away.
- Remember that you are not responsible for other people's problems, and let them find their own way.
- Hold your ideas, values, and preferences confidently, even if others disagree with them.
- Look beyond your initial impulsive reactions, so you can see your real intentions and act in ways that match who you want to be instead of what your impulses dictate.

Add some of your own:

______________________________

______________________________

______________________________

______________________________

______________________________

*Entering an intimate relationship to gain approval or validation is risky because it can mean failing to set proper boundaries. It might mean allowing yourself to be treated in ways that are unacceptable to you.*

**You can** never get from another person what you should be giving to yourself. Circle some of the things you should be giving to yourself that you haven't been:

| | | |
|---|---|---|
| Love | Acceptance | Validation |
| Understanding | Caring | Respect |
| Motivation | The benefit of the doubt | Honesty |
| Confidence | Accountability | Goals |
| Laughter | Relaxation Breaks | Joy |
| Happiness | | |

Add some of your own:

Every block of stone has a statue inside it, and it is the task of the sculptor to discover it . . . in every block of marble I see a statue as plain as though it stood before me, shaped and perfect in attitude and action. I have only to hew away the rough walls that imprison the lovely apparition to reveal it to the other eyes as mine to see it.

~Michelangelo

Just as the artist can see the sculpture within the block of stone, you should see the potential inside of yourself, even if you haven't manifested it yet. Often, all we know of ourselves is a block of unfinished person. We don't know how to chisel away the massive rock that's hiding our beauty.

Make a list of the qualities you have that you don't want to change:

*. . . you begin loving yourself when you start to create who you are in every situation you face.*

Loving yourself comes more easily when you learn to accept what happens in your life as part of the growth process that unlocks your potential. When you love yourself, you face life head-on and don't hide behind people-pleasing behaviors. You're able to overcome the setbacks you encounter, because you have faith in your ability to get through them.

My biggest challenge in the past:

How did I get through it?

My current biggest challenge:

How can I overcome it?

*You're never too old,
never too bad, never too
late, never too sick, to
start from scratch
once again.*

*~Bikram Choudhury*

Here are some questions you can ask yourself when an opportunity for people-pleasing arises:

- What would my best self like to do right now?
- What actions would make me happier?
- What type of person do I want to be in this situation?
- What do I want to do?

Add some of your own questions:

*To let go does not mean to get rid of. To let go means to let be. When we let be with compassion, things come and go on their own.*

*~Jack Kornfield*

Holding on to pain doesn't fix anything. Constantly replaying the past in your mind doesn't undo what's been done. Wishing things were different doesn't make them so. In some cases, especially when it comes to the past, all you can do is accept whatever it is you're holding on to, and then let it go.

Meditate on the things you've been holding on to that you know you need to release. Give some thought to some ways that you can let go, whether it's by forgiving, saying goodbye, or resolving an unresolved conflict.

Write your ideas here:

*With forgiveness, your victim identity dissolves, and your true power emerges.*

~ Eckhart Tolle

If you're stuck in the past and can't let go of things that happened to you, chances are you believe the things your abusers, bullies, or other negative people in your life believe about you. If you don't let go of their ideas about you, you'll stay imprisoned by them, unable to live up to your full potential.

Ideas to keep in mind:

- Other people's thoughts and ideas about you have more to do with them—their beliefs, issues, and opinions—than with you.
- Other people's viewpoints are manifestations of their unresolved issues and anxieties; they have no bearing on the facts of who you are.
- Putting others' opinions above your own ideas about yourself devalues your worth and makes their word stronger than yours.
- Your ideas, and the way you experience yourself, need to take center stage.

Add some of your thoughts here:

*The moment you start living your own life, for yourself, will be a definitive one for your future. But don't be surprised if you start feeling like people are waiting in line to tear you down because of it.*

While people may not consciously or intentionally try to harm you, they'll try everything to get you back in a position where you'll be available to please them. Since your people-pleasing nature has led certain people to rely heavily on you, those people will get anxious when you don't comply—and when those anxious people believe you're the cause of their anxiety, they'll likely get angry with you.

Here are some affirmations to repeat to yourself when you're feeling anxious and guilty about putting yourself first:

- I am not doing anything wrong; I am doing what is best for me and my life.
- I am not selfish for choosing not to do something I don't want to do.
- I am not a bad person for considering my needs.
- I am still a good and giving person; I'm just doing it on my terms now.
- I can be a good person and have someone be angry with me at the same time.
- I am worthy, valuable, and deserving of happiness.

Add some of your own affirmations here:

*Happy couples handle conflict constructively to advance the goals and needs of the relationship.*

*~Harriet B. Braiker, Ph.D.*

People-pleasers avoid conflict at all costs, which keeps their relationships from reaching a deeper level. When you learn how to have conflict constructively, you not only benefit from feeling better, you also gain experience in self-regulation, which helps you thoughtfully consider helpful responses to the situation at hand. By approaching conflict more constructively, you help mutual understanding to grow in your relationships, which may lead to fewer problems in the future.

How can you keep in mind that it's ok to sometimes have conflict in your relationships?

How can you avoid taking the full blame for conflicts that might occur in your relationships?

*"Be not afraid of growing slowly,*
*be afraid only of standing still."*

*~ Chinese Proverb*

*Destructive conflict is an upsetting and draining experience; so if you've been attempting to ignore it, that's perfectly logical.*

Four Things to Remember When Overcoming Your Fear of Confrontation:

- **Don't Bury Your Feelings:** Start seeing your inclination to avoid confrontation as the primary indication of relationship trouble.
- **Remember That Conflict is Inevitable:** Don't judge yourself or think something's wrong with your relationship if a conflict occurs.
- **Work Through Your Fear:** Remind yourself that there's no need to be afraid. Instead, find effective and helpful ways to communicate.
- **Stop Overestimating Other People's Anger:** Your fear of confrontation causes you to overestimate how angry others will get when you express yourself to them.

Who have you been hiding from or avoiding in your life? What would you like to say to that person?

*Remember: despite how open, peaceful, and loving you attempt to be, people can only meet you as deeply as they've met themselves.*

*~ Matt Kahn*

It's essential to keep in mind that you are changing your people-pleasing ways so that you can put more of your energy into your own life, not so that you can change others.

List the relationships in your life that you cherish the most.

______________________________________________

______________________________________________

______________________________________________

______________________________________________

______________________________________________

What is it about the people in these relationships that allows you to connect so meaningfully with them?

______________________________________________

______________________________________________

______________________________________________

______________________________________________

How can you continue to experience those relationships as a resource?

______________________________________________

______________________________________________

______________________________________________

______________________________________________

*Accept everything about yourself; I mean everything. You are you, and that is the beginning and the end, no apologies, no regrets.*

*~ Clark Moustakas*

Self-full people have relationships that are fulfilling and satisfying. They maintain solid boundaries and have a clear idea of who they are, so that their relationships don't become draining or overwhelming.

Circle the boundaries that you need to work on:

Knowing your limits

Knowing that you are worthy

Mastering setting boundaries

Making time for yourself

Holding others accountable

Being Firm

Applying boundaries

Changing your role

Speaking up

Write about what it would look like for you to set boundaries:

*You must change how you react to people before you can change how you interact with them.*

~Rick Kirschner

There's a saying that goes, "People who irritate us usually have something to show us about ourselves." Whenever someone irritates you, ask yourself: What is this person bringing out in me that I don't want to see? If it's a family member, close friend, or intimate partner who's challenging you, think about your own behavior in the relationship. Have you contributed to the situation by saying yes instead of no too many times? Have you failed to communicate that something was bothering you?

After giving this some thought, write about the changes you'd like to make in how you react to others.

*Even if you're on the right track, you'll get run over if you just sit there.*

*~Will Rogers*

Below are some valuable lessons for people-pleasers; highlight the ones that you need to learn the most:

- People can learn to do things for themselves, if you let them.
- If you're going to confront someone, wait until you've calmed down and can rationally express yourself.
- Do your part in your relationships, and lend a hand to others without doing things for them.
- Accept people for who they are, even if you disagree with their decisions.
- When you're upset with someone, look at the part you played in the conflict—not to take the blame, but to take responsibility for yourself.
- Try to genuinely listen to others—not to come up with a response, but to genuinely hear what they have to say.
- Notice when you get the impulse to overly involve yourself in others' lives. When you feel the urge, resist it and occupy yourself with something else.
- When you have to tell someone disappointing news, stick to the facts. Leading with your emotions will only make things worse.
- Add some of your own lessons:

______________________________

______________________________

______________________________

______________________________

______________________________

*People who change the world have declared independence from other people's expectations!*

As director and author Benjamin Mee said,

"You know, sometimes all you need is twenty seconds of insane courage. Just literally twenty seconds of just embarrassing bravery. And I promise you, something great will come of it."

Sit silently for 15 minutes and contemplate what you would do if you were no longer afraid. Write out a plan to do these things here.

*Everyone thinks of changing the world, but no one thinks of changing himself.*

*~Leo Tolstoy*

**Reflect on this:** What difference would it make if you tried to understand the role you've played in your relationships, and how would it benefit you to change that role? People tend to concern themselves with external things they can't control, when instead they should be looking within. Spend some time looking inside yourself and deciding what role you want to play as a family member, friend, employee, or person in general. Who is it you want to be in relation to others?

After you decide this, use your life experiences as a way to practice being the person you'd like to be. The only way to do this is by being with others and exploring new ways of relating to them.

Ask yourself:

How can I change my response to people without taking the blame?

How can I act more for myself?

*This above all: to thine own self be true, And it must follow, as the night the day, Thou canst not then be false to any man.*

*~ William Shakespeare*

Take a moment to close your eyes and honestly think about what brings you joy. Write those things down here, and then direct your thoughts and actions toward creating a more joyous life.

# Acknowledgements

My warm appreciation to all of the people who helped me create this reflective journal.

My editor, Dr. Denise Fournier, for taking the time to thoughtfully edit my work.

My book designer, Chris Molé, for the beautiful design of this journal.

My friend, Natalie Cormier, for taking the time to read through my work and give me constructive feedback.

My friends and family, who continue to support me on my journey to living life as an authentic expression of who I am.

# About the Author

Dr. Ilene S. Cohen, Ph.D. is a psychotherapist, author, and mother of two animated young girls. She is one of the most respected voices in the psychology of people-pleasing and navigating the difficulty of living an intentional life while trying to maintain fulfilling relationships. She is the author of 5 books, all of which have received awards and 5-star ratings from her readers. These include her most famous book, *When It's Never About You,* and her new book, *Anxious for Answers*. She's a regular contributor to *Psychology Today,* with dedicated readers numbering in the millions. Her books and therapy practice are fueled by a passion for helping people achieve their goals, build a strong sense of self, and lead fulfilling and meaningful lives. As president of her family's foundation, Dr. Ilene oversees various initiatives geared toward creating better opportunities for those in need.

To contact Dr. Ilene directly, you can visit her website, www.doctorilene.com.

CPSIA information can be obtained
at www.ICGtesting.com
Printed in the USA
LVHW071625201122
733613LV00009B/215

9 780999 311549